·THE· ·ORCHARD·

For Glynn Boyd Harte

ORCHARD BOOKS
96 Leonard Street, London EC2A 4RH
Orchard Books Australia
14 Mars Road, Lane Cove, NSW 2066
ISBN 1 86039 413 2 (paperback)
ISBN 1 85213 473 9 (hardback)
First published in Great Britain 1994
First paperback publication 1997
Illustrations © Ian Beck 1994
The right of Ian Beck to be identified as the Illustrator
of this Work has been asserted by him in accordance
with the Copyright, Designs and Patents Act, 1988.
A CIP catalogue record for this book is available
from the British Library.
Printed in Belgium

·THE· ·ORCHARD· A B C

·IAN·BECK·

ORCHARD BOOKS

Aa

A is for alligator, Aladdin, acrobat, apple, anchor, avocado and ant

Bb

B is for bear, Bo-peep, basket, baby, bird, balloon,
butterfly, bricks, boat and ball

C is for cat, clown, crabs, cake, candle,
cliffs and clouds

Dd

D is for duck, drum and daisies

Ee

E is for elephant, envelope and eggshell

F is for fox, flute, fountain, fireworks, frog and fan

Gg

G is for gorilla, guitar, goose, grapes, glasses and grass

Hh

H is for Humpty-Dumpty, hippopotamus, house, hen and hyacinths

I is for imp and ink

J is for Jack and Jill, Jack and the Beanstalk and
jack-in-the-box

K is for king, kangaroo, kiwi, koala, kite and key

L l

L is for lion, Little Red Riding Hood, lemons,
lighthouse, ladder, leaves and ladybird

Mm

M is for monkey, mouse, mirror, mushrooms, moon, mask, magnet and mountains

N is for Noah's Ark

Oo

O is for Old King Cole, ostrich, octopus, orange,
onion and owl

P p

P is for Puss-in-Boots, pig, pumpkin, parasol, parrot, pears, pansies and palace

Q q

Q is for queen, quail, quill and question mark

R r

R is for robot, rocking-horse, rainbow, rocket,
reins and rope

Ss

S is for sun, sea, sand, sailor, spade, starfish,
sandcastle and star

T is for toad, teddy-bear, toucan, Tom Thumb, toothbrush, trumpet and tree

U is for unicorn, umbrella and Ugly Duckling

V is for vulture, violin, volcano and violets

Ww

W is for woodcutter, woods, windmill, witch and well

X is the ending for fox and for box

Y is for yak, yawn, yoghurt and yo-yo

Z is for zebras zzzz-ing

A B C D E F

G H I J K L M

N O P Q R S T

U V W X Y Z